# The Working Body

Nuala Mullan and Kirk Bizley

Heinemann
LIBRARY

**www.heinemann.co.uk/library**
Visit our website to find out more information about Heinemann Library books.

To order:
☎ Phone ++44 (0) 1865 888066
▤ Send a fax to ++44 (0) 1865 314091
▦ Visit the Heinemann Bookshop at www.heinemann.co.uk/library to browse our catalogue and order online.

First published in Great Britain by Heinemann Library, Halley Court, Jordan Hill, Oxford OX2 8EJ, part of Harcourt Education. Heinemann is a registered trademark of Harcourt Education Ltd.

© Harcourt Education Ltd 1999, 2007
2nd Edition first published in paperback in 2008.
The moral right of the proprietor has been asserted.

Editorial: Andrew Farrow
Design: Joanna Hinton-Malivoire
Picture research: Hannah Taylor
Production: Duncan Gilbert

Originated by Dot Gradations Ltd
Printed and bound in China by CTPS

ISBN 978 0 4310 7877 9 (hardback)
12 11 10 09 07
10 9 8 7 6 5 4 3 2

ISBN 978 0 4310 7884 7 (paperback)
12 11 10 09 08
10 9 8 7 6 5 4 3 2 1

**British Library Cataloguing in Publication Data**
Mullan, Nuala and Bizley, Kirk
The working body. – 2nd ed. – (Aspects of P. E.)
612'.044
A full catalogue record for this book is available from the British Library.

**Acknowledgements**
The publishers would like to thank the following for permission to reproduce photographs:
Action Plus pp. **27** (Steve Bardens), **29** (Mike Hewitt); Allsport pp. **5** (Mike Hewitt), **11** (Mike Cooper); Corbis pp. **15** (Reuters/Alessandro Bianchi), **42** (Reuters); Empics (Michael Steele) pp. **6**, **7**, **31**; Gareth Bowden pp. **21**, **23**; Redferns (Mick Hutson) p. **9**; Science Photo Library pp. **14** (AJ Photo), **22** (Saturn Stills); Sporting Pictures (UK) Ltd p. **4**.

Cover photograph of Kirsten Bolm of Germany, competing in the women's 100m hurdles at the European Cup, 2005, reproduced with permission of Getty Images (Bongarts/Alexander Hassenstein).

The authors and publishers would like to thank Derek Ball, Lynn Booth, Phil and Pat Bradbeer, Sonia Cross, Barry Fischer, Neil Fowler, Keith George, Sue Jones, Trevor Lea, Marie Mullan, Doug Neate and Joan Simcox for their help and comments during the preparation of the first edition of this book.

Every effort has been made to contact copyright holders of any material reproduced in this book. Any omissions will be rectified in subsequent printings if notice is given to the publishers.

**Disclaimer**
All the Internet addresses (URLs) given in this book were valid at the time of going to press. However, due to the dynamic nature of the Internet, some addresses may have changed, or sites may have changed or ceased to exist since publication. While the author and publishers regret any inconvenience this may cause readers, no responsibility for any such changes can be accepted by either the author or the publishers.

To Lola, my dearest granddaughter, from Kirk

# Contents

Any words appearing in the text in bold, **like this**, are explained in the glossary.

The human body is made up of many complex parts. These parts must work together to form an integrated unit. As human beings, we grow, reproduce, move, obtain energy from food, react to changes and get rid of waste products. Even a simple movement such as hitting a ball with a racquet needs a complex series of events for it to occur in a co-ordinated fashion.

To understand how our bodies move, we need to study the basic structure of the body and how its parts work together so that movement can occur. This helps us to appreciate what is going on in the body when someone exercises or plays sport.

## Components of the body

Bodies come in many different sizes and shapes, and each body is unique. However, the basic parts of the body are the same for everyone. The body is made up of **cells**, tissues, **organs** and organ systems:

- A cell is the basic unit of life that can maintain itself, grow and reproduce.

All cells have some common characteristics. They also have individual characteristics that make them a specific type of cell, such as a muscle or nerve cell.

- A tissue is a collection of similar types of cells. For example, muscle tissue is made up of many muscle cells.

- An organ is a collection of different tissues that work together. For example, the heart contains muscle tissue as well as **connective tissue**.

- An organ system is a group of organs that work together to do a certain job.

The body is made up of a number of organ systems:

- The respiratory system takes oxygen into the cells so that energy can be released.

- The circulatory system carries blood around the body, protects against disease and maintains body temperature.

- The digestive system breaks food down into small pieces so that it can enter the blood and be distributed around the body.

- The nervous system senses changes, interprets them and responds. It is the main control system of the body.

- The skeletal system protects, supports and gives shape to the body. It also produces blood and allows movement to occur.

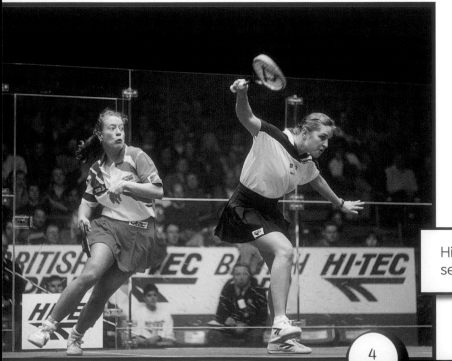

Hitting a ball requires a complex series of movements.

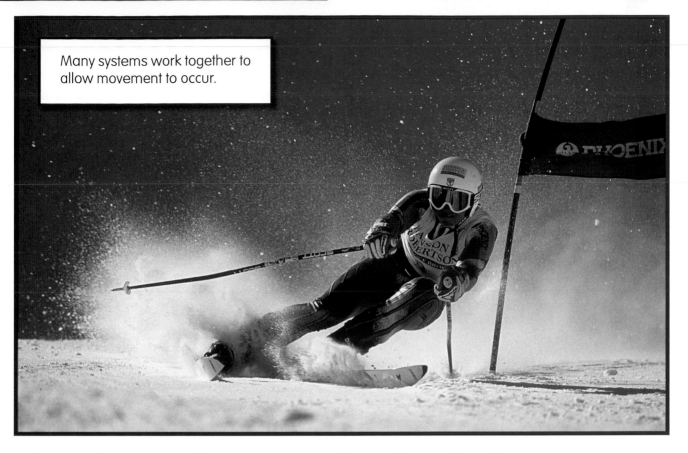

Many systems work together to allow movement to occur.

- The muscular system produces movement and helps maintain posture.

- The endocrine system releases chemicals called hormones that control various functions of the body.

- The excretory system removes waste products from the body.

- The reproductive system enables reproduction to take place.

- The lymphatic system defends the body against disease.

These systems make up the whole of the body. Together, they keep the body working properly.

## Movement

To do any form of exercise we must move, and this needs a muscle contraction. For any form of movement, the muscle needs a signal telling it to contract, and energy to do this.

The signal comes from the nervous system and the energy comes from food. The muscle also needs oxygen.

The respiratory system brings air into the body and the circulatory system carries the oxygen from the air to the muscles that need it.

The digestive system breaks food down. The food is absorbed by the blood, so that the circulatory system can take it to the cells that need it.

Energy is released from the food, with the help of oxygen. The muscle can contract and the bones to which it is attached can move.

This series of events, involving the muscular system, nervous system, respiratory system, circulatory system, digestive system and skeletal system, has to take place for any movement to occur.

During movement, muscles need a constant supply of energy. This energy is in the form of a substance called adenosine triphosphate (ATP). There is some ATP present in the muscles, but there is not enough to supply all the energy needed for most sport or exercise. Therefore, the **cells** in the muscles need to make more ATP so that the muscles can contract again and again. The cells produce the necessary energy in two ways:

- **anaerobic** energy is obtained without using oxygen.

- **aerobic** energy is obtained by using oxygen.

## Anaerobic energy

Anaerobic energy can be produced by two systems: the phosphagen system or the lactic acid system.

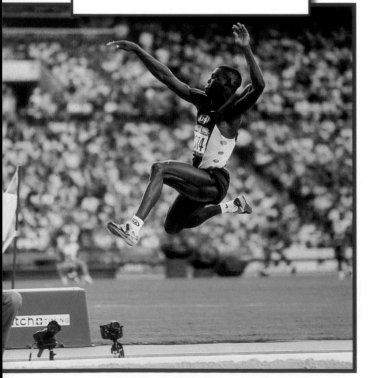

Long jumpers use anaerobic energy to jump.

Using the phosphagen system the energy is provided by means of compounds called phosphates that are in the muscle cells. This energy is produced very quickly, but the stores of phosphates in the cells are small – so the amount of energy supplied is limited. This way of producing usually takes place for very short, explosive activities such as a short sprint, a javelin throw or the long jump.

The second way of producing energy without oxygen is through the lactic acid system. This uses carbohydrate as the fuel. Carbohydrate is stored in the muscles as glycogen. When glycogen is broken down, energy is produced – with lactic acid as a by-product.

glycogen $\longrightarrow$ energy + lactic acid

Lactic acid can cause fatigue if it builds up in the muscle, so this system cannot supply energy on its own for very long. The lactic acid system is the main system used in activities where you are working at your maximum for between one and three minutes, such as a 400 m or 800 m sprint.

## Aerobic energy

Aerobic energy is produced in the muscle cells, using oxygen. Glycogen is broken down to produce energy, carbon dioxide and water.

glycogen + oxygen $\longrightarrow$ energy + carbon dioxide + water

Fat can also be broken down in the presence of oxygen to produce energy. The aerobic system is a lot slower than the anaerobic system, but it gives you a plentiful supply of energy. The carbon dioxide produced is removed from your body through the respiratory system. The aerobic system is the main energy system for longer, less intense endurance activities, such as the marathon.

# Oxygen uptake

The amount of oxygen that your body takes in and uses at any time is called the volume of oxygen uptake ($VO^2$). Your oxygen uptake increases as you work harder. Everyone has a maximum ability to take in and use oxygen. This is called their maximum oxygen uptake ($VO^2$ max). Endurance training will improve your maximum oxygen uptake, but some people are able to achieve a higher $VO^2$ max than others. This is due to physical differences that are inherited from your parents. The top endurance athletes have very high $VO^2$ max values as a result of hard training, but also because they inherited the right physical characteristics from their parents.

The different energy systems work together to supply energy. Which system your body brings into play will depend on how long and how hard you exercise.

# Recovery process

After exercising, your breathing rate stays high (more oxygen is breathed in) and your heart continues to beat fast. Gradually both of these will return to normal. The term **oxygen debt** is used to describe the need for extra oxygen uptake (above resting levels) that occurs during recovery.

Your body uses extra oxygen to release energy to rebuild the anaerobic compounds that were broken down at the start of exercise and to help remove lactic acid from your muscles.

During recovery from exercise, the breathing rate remains high. Professional athletes include a proper cool-down as part of their training to ensure that the body returns to normal at a safe, gentle pace.

## Cooling down

A cool-down (also called a warm-down) aims to bring the heart rate and oxygen uptake gradually back to resting levels. During a cool-down you continue to exercise at a gentle pace that keeps the blood circulating around the body faster than if you stopped suddenly. The circulating blood removes the unwanted lactic acid from your muscles more quickly and helps reduce muscle stiffness after exercise.

# The respiratory system

To keep working, the body needs to get air inside and supply oxygen to wherever it is needed. The body also needs to get rid of some gases that build up inside. Together these are the jobs of the respiratory system. The respiratory system is made up of several **organs**.

## Mouth and nose

Air enters your body through your mouth (buccal cavity) and nose (nasal cavity). These are separated by the palate at the top of the mouth. These two cavities join up at the back of your mouth and air passes from both of them into the **pharynx** (throat).

When air enters your nasal cavity through the nose, it is warmed, moistened and filtered. Hairs inside the nose trap any large dust particles. The air then passes into the upper nasal cavity, which is lined with **mucous membranes**. These membranes release a thick fluid called mucus. The mucus moistens the air and traps smaller dust particles, preventing them from travelling further into your body.

When you are resting, you breathe most air in through your nose. During exercise you need to get a lot of air inside, so you breathe air in through both your mouth and nose.

## Pharynx

Your pharynx (throat) is a passageway for air and food. It is also where you produce speech sounds. Food passes towards the

The respiratory system.

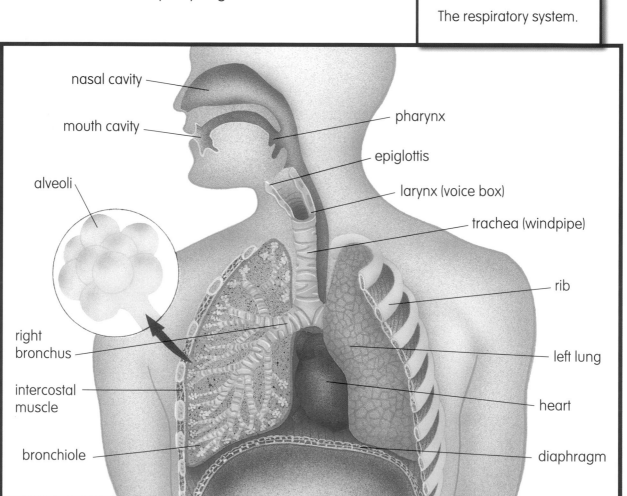

nasal cavity

mouth cavity

pharynx

epiglottis

alveoli

larynx (voice box)

trachea (windpipe)

rib

right bronchus

intercostal muscle

left lung

heart

bronchiole

diaphragm

food pipe (oesophagus) and air passes towards the windpipe (trachea) via the voice box (larynx).

# Larynx

Your larynx is a short passageway connecting your throat to your windpipe. Inside the larynx are the vocal cords. These are folds of mucous membrane that vibrate when air passes through, producing sound waves. The sound then resonates in your pharynx, nose and mouth and is converted into speech.

# Epiglottis

At the top of the larynx is a flap called the **epiglottis**, which acts like a gate. Its job is to allow air to pass into the larynx and to prevent food from getting through. When you swallow, the epiglottis closes over the top of the larynx so that food goes down the food pipe and not into the larynx. If your food does go down the wrong way, the process has not worked and you cough to bring the food back up into your throat.

# Trachea

Your trachea (windpipe) is a passageway (12 cm long) that connects your larynx to your lungs. It is surrounded by incomplete rings of **cartilage** that prevent the wall from collapsing and obstructing airflow. When you swallow, the food pipe expands slightly into the gaps in the cartilage of the trachea.

The vocal cords are used to produce the sounds in singing.

## Vocal pitch

The pitch of the voice is controlled by the tension in the vocal cords. When the tension is greater, the pitch is higher. The vocal cords in men are usually thicker and longer and vibrate more slowly than in women. This is why men's voices generally have a lower pitch than women's.

# Bronchi and bronchioles

The trachea divides into two passageways that lead into the lungs. The right bronchus (see diagram on page 8) leads to the right lung and the left bronchus leads to the left lung. The left and right bronchus together are called bronchi. Because it is shorter, more vertical and wider than the left bronchus, foreign objects are more likely to enter the right bronchus. These bronchi divide into smaller bronchi in the lungs, and these divide into smaller tubes called bronchioles. This network of tubes is called the bronchial tree because the network of passageways looks like the branches of a tree.

# Alveoli

The bronchioles lead into millions of tiny air sacs called **alveoli**. Gas exchange of oxygen and carbon dioxide takes place in the alveoli (see page 12).

# Lungs

Your bronchi, bronchioles and alveoli together make up your lungs. The two lungs are the link between the outside air and the blood. The liver lies below the right lung, which is shorter than the left lung.

Each lung is surrounded by a double-layered membrane called the **pleural membrane**. The outer layer is attached to the wall of the rib cage (thoracic cage) and the inner layer covers the lungs. The space between these layers is called the pleural cavity. The membranes release a lubricating fluid into the pleural cavity to allow them to move smoothly against one another during breathing. If these layers become inflamed it creates friction between them, which can cause pain.

# Thoracic cage

The lungs are surrounded by your thoracic cage (rib cage), which protects the lungs and heart from physical damage. The thoracic cage is made up of twelve pairs of ribs. In between the ribs are two layers of muscles, called the **internal and external intercostals**, that are involved in the breathing process. The space inside the thoracic cage is called the thoracic cavity.

# Diaphragm

Beneath your lungs is a large, dome-shaped muscle called the **diaphragm**. It separates the thoracic cavity from other organs such as the stomach and liver. This muscle plays an important role in the breathing process.

## Irritations

Coughing is a reflex action that sends air rushing through the respiratory passages. A cough can be triggered by a foreign body lodged in the trachea, larynx or epiglottis.

A sneeze is set off by an irritation of the mucus in the nose. It is a sudden contraction of the internal intercostal muscles and it forcefully expels air through the mouth and nose.

A hiccup is a sudden contraction of the diaphragm and rapid closure of the epiglottis, producing a sharp sound. It is usually triggered by irritation of the nerves associated with the digestive system.

# The breathing process

The breathing process brings fresh air into your lungs and removes waste products such as carbon dioxide and water vapour from your body. Breathing in is called inspiration (or inhalation) and breathing out is called expiration (or exhalation).

The movement of air into and out of your lungs is called ventilation. When resting, the breathing rate of an adult is usually 12 breaths per minute. During exercise this rate increases to get more air into the lungs.

## Inspiration

When you breathe in, this is what happens:

- The diaphragm muscle contracts and flattens.

- The external intercostal muscles contract and pull the thoracic cage upwards and outwards.

- The volume inside the ribs increases and the pressure decreases.

- Air flows into the lungs.

## Expiration

When you have finished breathing in, this is what happens:

- The diaphragm and intercostal muscles relax.

- The dome of the diaphragm moves upwards and the thoracic cage moves downwards and inwards.

- The volume inside the ribs decreases and the pressure increases.

- Air flows out of the lungs.

Normally, breathing out is a passive process. That means it is not caused by muscles contracting. However, when you exercise hard, expiration becomes active. You need to use your stomach muscles and internal intercostal muscles to help force air out of your lungs.

## Respiration rates

During respiration your lungs give your body the oxygen it needs for any activity – even lying around! The average rate, if your age is 7 years or older, is 12–24 breaths per minute, and this will increase as you need more oxygen. Your respiration rate can increase up to 50 breaths per minute during periods of extreme exercise.

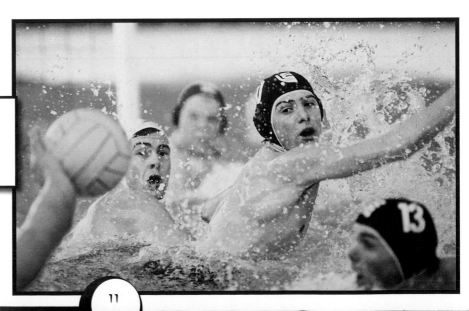

These water polo players are breathing hard to get air into their lungs.

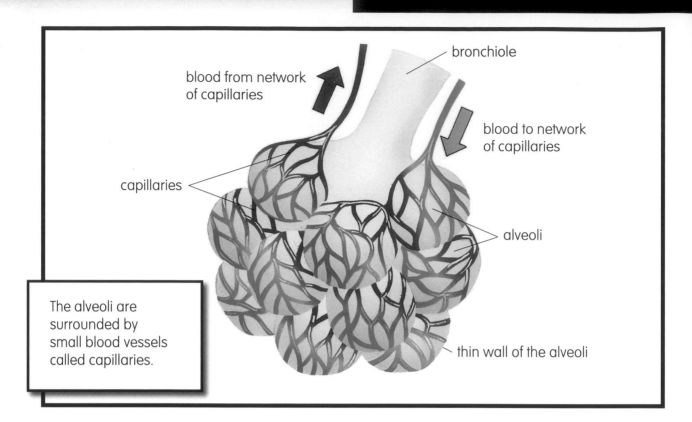

blood from network of capillaries

bronchiole

blood to network of capillaries

capillaries

alveoli

The alveoli are surrounded by small blood vessels called capillaries.

thin wall of the alveoli

# Composition of air

The air that we breathe is made up of a mixture of gases including nitrogen, oxygen and carbon dioxide. Inspired (breathed in) air is made up of 79.04 per cent nitrogen, 20.93 per cent oxygen and 0.03 per cent carbon dioxide.

When you take a breath in, these gases enter the mouth and nose and travel along the network of passageways into the alveoli. Here, the new air mixes with the air that is already in the alveoli from the last breath. This changes the composition of the air in the alveoli. Oxygen and carbon dioxide gas are exchanged between air and blood. This alters the levels of these gases in the air in the alveoli.

When you breathe out the composition of expired air is 79.61 per cent nitrogen, 16.89 per cent oxygen and 3.5 per cent carbon dioxide. This shows that the lungs are not very efficient at extracting oxygen.

For someone at rest, expired air still contains almost 17 per cent oxygen. During exercise, though, the amounts of oxygen taken in and carbon dioxide released will increase.

# Gas exchange

Inside the lungs, the alveoli are surrounded by millions of tiny blood vessels called **capillaries**. During gas exchange, oxygen passes from the alveoli to the blood in the capillaries and carbon dioxide passes from the blood to the alveoli. This movement of particles from an area of high concentration to an area of low concentration is known as **diffusion**.

The air in the alveoli is rich in oxygen and low in carbon dioxide, whereas the blood in the capillaries is low in oxygen and rich in carbon dioxide. As a result, oxygen diffuses from the air in the alveoli to the blood in the capillaries, and carbon dioxide diffuses in the opposite direction. Oxygen is then carried around your body to where it is needed and carbon dioxide is exhaled from the lungs.

The alveoli have several features that help gas exchange:

- *large surface area* – if all the alveoli in a pair of lungs were opened up and laid out flat on the ground, they would take up an area half the size of a tennis court! This means that there is a large surface for diffusion between the alveoli and blood.

- *thin walls* – so diffusion of gases through the walls is easier

- *moist lining* – helps with the diffusion of gases

- *surrounded by many capillaries* – also with thin walls to help diffusion.

# Effects of exercise

During exercise your body needs more oxygen to increase the energy production in the working muscles. To achieve this, you need to increase the rate and depth of breathing. This increases the amount of air moving into and out of your lungs (ventilation) and the amount of oxygen that is taken into your blood. As a result of the greater energy production, more carbon dioxide is produced and exhaled from your lungs.

There are two main, long-term benefits of exercise to the respiratory system. After training, the maximum amount of air that you can breathe in and out increases. This is called increased maximum ventilation, and it allows you to get more oxygen to the muscles and to do more exercise. Secondly, after training your body is more efficient at taking oxygen in and using it, so you do not need to breathe as much at a particular activity level as you did before. Both of these changes result from your improved **aerobic** fitness.

# Smoking

Although smoking cigarettes has been proven to be very harmful to health, it is still a common habit among many adults and young people. Cigarette smoking:

- reduces resistance of the lungs to disease, and often causes cancer

- irritates the passageways of the lungs and gradually destroys their lining

- increases airway resistance making breathing harder

- can be harmful to the baby of a pregnant mother.

Smoking also increases the demand for oxygen when exercising, because extra energy is needed for breathing. For people who do smoke, this effect can be reduced, short-term, by not smoking for a day before a big competition.

## Passive smoking

One of the dangers of smoking is that even non-smokers can be affected if they are in the immediate vicinity of smokers. If non-smokers inhale some of the smoke in the atmosphere, they can become 'passive smokers'. This means they can suffer the same damaging effects that smokers suffer. Passive smoking is one of the main reasons why there are now laws banning smoking in many public places.

Several techniques can be used to measure different types of lung volume, and to examine how well the lungs are functioning.

# Total lung capacity

Total lung capacity is the total amount of air that can be held in your lungs. It depends on the size of your lungs, and is made up of the vital capacity and the residual volume.

### Vital capacity

This is the largest amount of air that can be expired after a maximum inspiration. You can measure your vital capacity by taking a deep breath in and then blowing as much air as possible into a **spirometer**: a device for measuring gas volumes. The average value for the vital capacity of adults is 3–4 litres for women and 4–5 litres for men.

### Residual volume

Even when you breathe out as hard as you can, not all the air is expelled from your lungs. The residual volume is the volume of air that is left in the lungs after a maximum expiration. This is not easy to measure because the air remains in the lungs. The residual volume is normally about 25 per cent of the vital capacity. Average values for residual volumes of adults is 1–1.2 litres for women and 1.2–1.4 litres for men.

# Tidal volume

Tidal volume is the amount of air that you breathe in or out in one breath. At rest the tidal volume of an adult is about 0.5–1 litre, which means that 0.5–1 litre of air is breathed in or out in each breath. During exercise this can increase dramatically with the need to get more air into the body. You can achieve this by using some of the reserve volumes:

- Inspiratory reserve volume – the amount of air that can be forcefully inspired at the end of a normal inspiration.

- Expiratory reserve volume – the amount of air that can be forcefully expired at the end of a normal expiration.

It is possible to measure these volumes but they are not a good indicator of fitness. The size of the lungs cannot be altered by fitness training. The strength of the respiratory muscles can be affected, especially in sports such as swimming and scuba diving – where breathing is more forced and so the respiratory muscles work harder. However, the main influence on fitness is how efficient your respiratory system is at taking in oxygen and expelling carbon dioxide.

Measuring lung volumes can, however, give an indication of the health of the lungs and surrounding structures. Abnormal function may be the result of smoking or asthma. One test that is commonly used with asthma sufferers is the peak expiratory flow test.

The peak expiratory flow test.

# Peak expiratory flow

The peak expiratory flow is a measure of the maximum flow rate at which air can be expired from the lungs. It can be measured by blowing as fast as possible into a peak flow meter, which measures the speed of the air. If the flow of air is restricted in any way the value for peak flow will be reduced.

# Asthma

Asthma is a respiratory disease characterized by shortness of breath, wheezing and coughing. The airways in the lungs become narrow and this makes breathing difficult – a bit like breathing through a thin tube. People with asthma are extra-sensitive to certain irritants, such as pollen, dust and cold air, and to exercise. Most of the time, people suffering from asthma can breathe normally, but when an irritant affects the lungs it can bring on an asthma attack. This makes it difficult for the person to breathe out, so it is difficult to get air into the lungs. When this happens the person can start to breathe very rapidly and gasp for breath.

Most asthma sufferers use an inhaler. This is a simple device that allows the asthmatic to inhale a dose of medicine that will cause the airways to enlarge, allowing breathing to return to normal. During exercise more air has to be breathed in and out and this can trigger an attack, especially in cold weather. That is why you may see a person with asthma using an inhaler before exercising. Using an inhaler before exercise helps reduce the chances of an attack during exercise.

Many asthmatics use a peak expiratory flow meter daily to monitor the state of their airways. A lower-than-usual reading indicates that the airways are narrowed. The amount of medication taken can then be adjusted accordingly.

Marathon runner Paula Radcliffe has become world champion and world-record holder despite suffering from asthma. She won the world title in 2005, at this race in Helsinki, Finland.

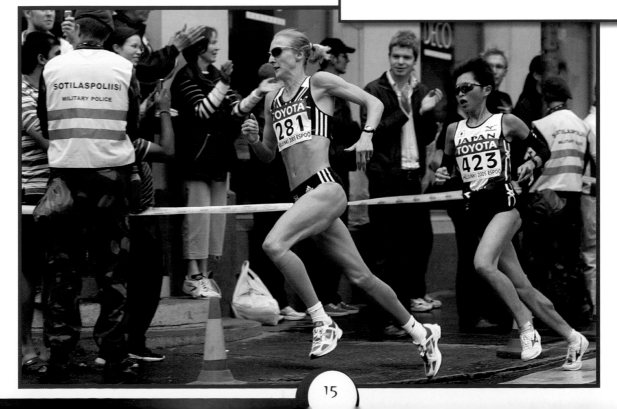

# 4 The circulatory system

The circulatory system is made up of the heart, blood and blood vessels. Its three main functions are:

- *transport of nutrients* (food) around the body and of oxygen and carbon dioxide to and from the lungs

- *protection* against disease by the production of antibodies

- *temperature regulation* by transporting heat from the centre of the body (core) to the skin or from the skin to the core. This is done to keep body temperature stable.

The network of blood vessels in the circulatory system ensures that blood reaches all parts of the body, carrying oxygen to working **cells** and carbon dioxide away from them.

## Heart

Your heart is the powerhouse of the circulatory system. Blood passes through the heart on its way to the tissues and again on its way back from the tissues, then on to the lungs. Each time your heart contracts, blood is pumped out and sent on its way.

The heart is made up of a specialized type of muscle called cardiac muscle. The structure of the heart consists of:

- **atria** (or auricles) – the two upper chambers: right atrium and left atrium

- **ventricles** – the two lower chambers: right and left ventricle

- **bicuspid (mitral) valve** – a one-way valve separating the left atrium from the left ventricle

- **tricuspid valve** – a one-way valve separating the right atrium and right ventricle.

The valves ensure blood flows through your heart in the correct direction. The right and left sides of the heart are separated by a wall so that blood cannot pass between one side and the other. Because of this the heart acts like two separate pumps.

## Blood flow through the heart

Blood that has come from the lungs is rich in oxygen and is called oxygenated blood (coloured red in the diagrams). This oxygenated blood follows a circuit around the body.

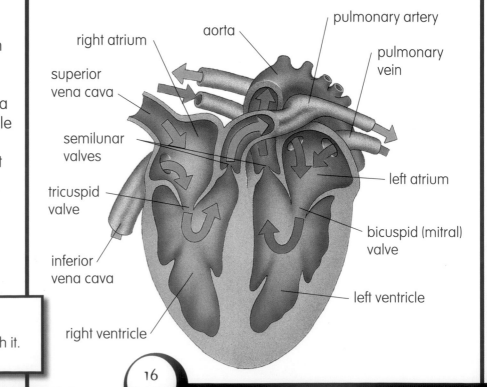

Structure of the heart and the direction of blood flow through it.

This is how the circuit works:

- Oxygenated blood enters the left atrium of the heart via large blood vessels called the **pulmonary veins**.

- The left atrium contracts and pushes the blood through the bicuspid valve into the left ventricle.

- The left ventricle then contracts and forces the blood out of the heart through a **semilunar valve**. The blood leaves the heart via a large blood vessel called the **aorta**.

- The tissues around the body take oxygen out of the blood. This blood is now called deoxygenated blood (coloured blue in the diagrams).

- Deoxygenated blood returns to the heart via two large blood vessels, called the **superior and inferior vena cava**, which empty into the right atrium.

- The right atrium contracts, forcing blood into the right ventricle through the tricuspid valve.

- The right ventricle contracts, pumping blood out of the heart through a semilunar valve. The deoxygenated blood leaves the heart via the **pulmonary artery** and returns to the lungs. Here, carbon dioxide is exchanged for oxygen and the circuit is repeated.

Because it is constantly circulating around the body, blood is passing through both sides of the heart at the same time. Both atria contract at the same time, then both ventricles contract at the same time. Together these events make up a heart beat. The heart is then relaxed until the cycle begins again. During exercise this circuit has to be completed much more quickly, so the period of relaxation between beats is much shorter.

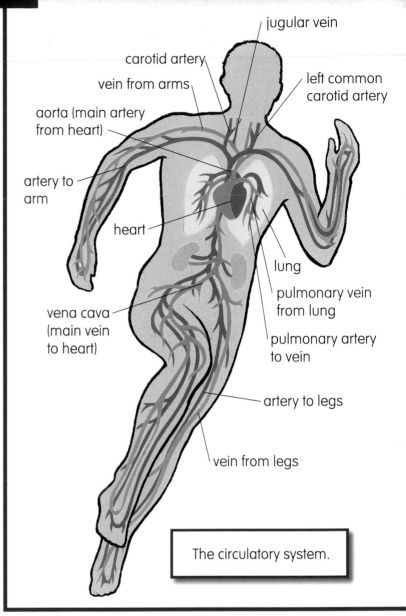

jugular vein

carotid artery

vein from arms

left common carotid artery

aorta (main artery from heart)

artery to arm

heart

lung

pulmonary vein from lung

vena cava (main vein to heart)

pulmonary artery to vein

artery to legs

vein from legs

The circulatory system.

## Heart rates

A normal resting heart rate for an adult is around 70 beats per minute. This means that the heart beats more than 100,000 times per day, pumping 7,000 litres of blood around 96,000 kilometres of blood vessels.

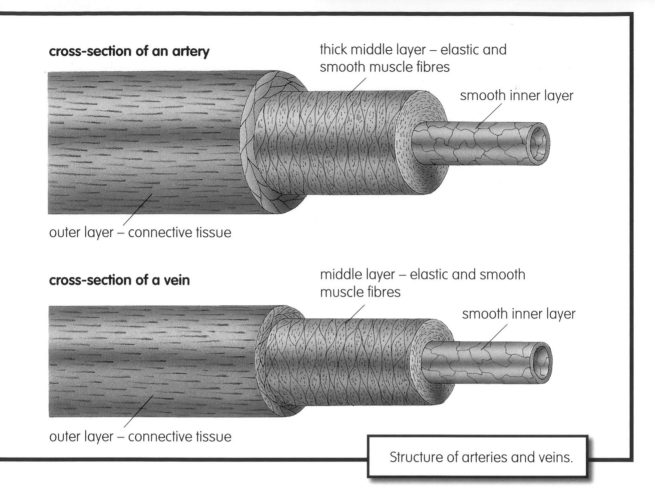

**cross-section of an artery**

thick middle layer – elastic and smooth muscle fibres

smooth inner layer

outer layer – connective tissue

**cross-section of a vein**

middle layer – elastic and smooth muscle fibres

smooth inner layer

outer layer – connective tissue

Structure of arteries and veins.

# Pulmonary and systemic circulation

The flow of blood around your body is called circulation:

- Pulmonary circulation is the circuit of blood between your lungs and heart. It carries deoxygenated blood from the right ventricle to the lungs where carbon dioxide is released and oxygen taken up from the **alveoli**. The oxygenated blood is then carried from the lungs to the left atrium of the heart.

- Systemic circulation is the link between your heart and the rest of your body. Oxygenated blood leaves the left ventricle and is transported around your body to your muscles, brain, kidneys, liver and other tissues. Your **organs** and tissues extract oxygen from the blood and deposit carbon

dioxide. The deoxygenated blood then returns to the right atrium of your heart.

The walls of the left ventricle have a thicker layer of muscle than the right ventricle because it has to pump blood around your body, whereas the right ventricle only has to pump blood as far as your lungs.

# Blood vessels

Blood vessels are a network of tubes that carry blood around your body. There are different types with individual functions.

## Arteries

Arteries are blood vessels that carry blood away from your heart. The pulmonary artery carries blood from the heart to the lungs. The aorta is an artery that carries blood from the heart to the rest of your body. This large artery divides into smaller arteries that branch out in different directions. These then subdivide into even smaller arteries called **arterioles**, which lead to tissues throughout the body. The centre of an artery or vein that the blood flows through is called the **lumen**.

The walls of arteries have three layers:

• a smooth inner layer

• a thick middle layer of elastic and smooth muscle fibres

• an outer layer of **connective tissue**.

The thick muscle layer means that the arteries can cope with the pressure of the blood being pumped out of your heart. It also means that blood flow along an artery can be controlled. When the muscles contract the lumen is reduced and less blood can flow through. This is called **vasoconstriction**. When the muscle layer is relaxed, the size of the lumen is increased and more blood can flow through. This is called **vasodilation**. These processes allow the amount of blood flowing to different parts of your body to be controlled.

## Veins

Veins are blood vessels that carry blood to your heart. Small veins called **venules** join up to form larger veins. The pulmonary vein carries blood to the heart from the lungs. The superior and inferior vena cava carry blood to your heart from around your body.

The walls of veins have the same three layers as arteries, but the thickness of the layers is different. The middle and outer layers are thinner than in an artery.

One major difference between veins and arteries is that veins have valves. Blood that is returning to the heart from around your body is at a lower pressure than the blood flowing from it. This low pressure is not enough to push the blood back to the heart. The valves in your veins prevent any backflow of blood. In the upper part of your body, gravity helps push blood back to the heart. The contraction of the muscles surrounding the veins also helps squeeze blood back to your heart.

## Capillaries

Capillaries are the connection between arterioles and venules. They form a network of very fine tubes around tissues and allow small particles to pass from the blood into the tissues, and vice versa. The walls of capillaries are only one cell thick, which makes it easier for **diffusion** to take place.

### Fatty arteries

In some people, fat may accumulate on the walls of the arteries and partially obstruct blood flow. The medical name for this build-up of fat is **atherosclerosis**. People who smoke, eat a lot of fatty food or are inactive are at greater risk from atherosclerosis. When this happens in the arteries of the heart, it is called coronary artery disease or heart disease.

# Blood

Blood plays a vital role in transporting substances, such as oxygen, around your body, regulating temperature and fighting disease. On average an adult male has 5–6 litres and an adult female has 4–5 litres of blood in their body. For a person with a blood volume of 5 litres, at any one time 1 litre will be in the lungs, 3 litres in the veins of the systemic circulation and 1 litre in the heart, systemic arteries and capillaries. Blood is made up of mainly:

• red blood cells

• white blood cells

• plasma.

## Red blood cells

Red blood cells (erythrocytes) normally make up 40–47 per cent of blood. Their main function is to transport oxygen. **Haemoglobin** is a component of red blood cells and when it combines with oxygen, oxyhaemoglobin is formed. This is how oxygen is transported in the blood. Oxyhaemoglobin is a bright red compound that gives blood its colour. Red blood cells also play an important role in the transport of carbon dioxide.

Having more red blood cells means that more oxygen can be carried in the blood, which helps increase **aerobic** fitness. Some athletes train at high altitudes, which helps them develop the ability to carry more oxygen in their blood. However, the change is not permanent. Blood doping is a procedure that increases the number of red blood cells. Blood is removed from the athlete and stored for a period of time. During this time the athlete's body makes more red blood cells to replace those lost. The stored blood is then injected back into the athlete, to raise the number of red cells in the blood. It is illegal for athletes to use this procedure.

## White blood cells

White blood cells (leucocytes) are outnumbered by red blood cells in a ratio of 600 to 1. They defend your body against disease by attacking foreign bodies or producing antibodies: substances that attack and destroy the foreign bodies.

## Plasma

Water is the main component of plasma (91 per cent) along with plasma proteins (7 per cent), salts and other substances. The plasma proteins have various functions including production of antibodies to fight

| Cells | Number per mm$^3$ | Produced in | Life span |
|---|---|---|---|
| red (erythrocytes) | 5 million | bone marrow | 120 days |
| white (leucocytes) | 5,000–10,000 | bone marrow and lymphatic tissue | few hours to few days |
| platelets (thrombocytes) | 250,000–400,000 | bone marrow | 5–9 days |

Table of characteristics of blood cells.

disease. They also aid in the process of blood clotting.

## Platelets

The third type of cells in the blood are called platelets (thrombocytes). They play an important role in blood clotting.

## Blood-clotting mechanism

Platelets gather and break down at the site of an injury. They release a chemical that results in the production of a substance called fibrin. Fibrin forms a network of long strands that trap blood cells and form a clot. This stops blood from escaping from a cut in your skin.

# Pulse locations

When your heart beats, blood is pumped around your body and causes the walls of the blood vessels to expand and then relax. This expansion is your pulse and can be felt at the following sites on your body:

- carotid pulse – just below the jaw on either side of your neck near the throat

- femoral pulse – in the groin area on either side of your pubic bone

- radial pulse – on the inside of your wrist just below the base of the thumb

- temporal pulse – on either side of your forehead in the temple area.

## Blood injuries

Many sports now have specific rules regarding blood injuries. In rugby, for example, if a player has a bleeding cut then they can be temporarily substituted or go to the 'blood bin'. This means they can be properly treated and there is no danger of the player contracting infections. The player can then return to the game when the injury has been dealt with.

You can take your own pulse before and after exercise. The radial pulse, on your wrist, is an easy one to try.

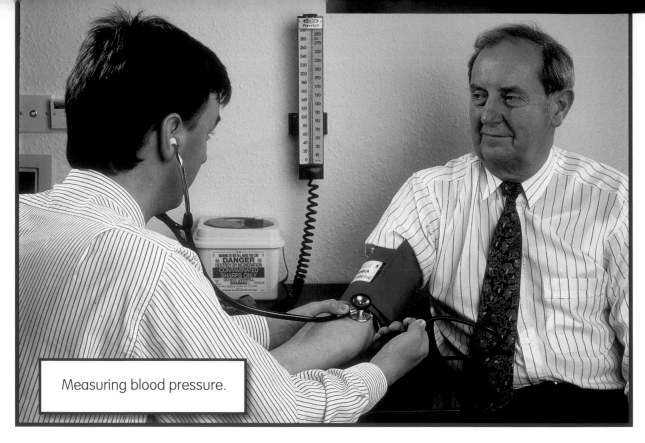

Measuring blood pressure.

# Blood pressure

When your heart contracts it forces blood out of itself and into the blood vessels. The force that the blood exerts on the walls of your blood vessels is called the blood pressure. Blood pressure changes depending on how much blood is pumped out of your heart and the resistance that the blood meets travelling through the blood vessels. As the blood travels away from your heart, friction between the blood and the walls of the arteries causes the blood pressure gradually to fall. Therefore, the blood pressure in the capillaries and veins is much lower than in the arteries.

In a healthy young person, the arteries are elastic and blood flows easily through them. As people get older this elasticity is lost and the resistance to blood flow is greater. This means that the heart has to pump harder to get blood around the body, so the blood pressure increases.

Blood pressure can be measured by using a stethoscope and a sphygmomanometer. This device consists of a cuff, an inflation bulb and a mercury column for the pressure readings. The cuff is placed around a person's arm and inflated until the blood supply is cut off. The pressure in the cuff is then slowly released and two pressure readings are taken when certain sounds are heard through the stethoscope. The two readings are:

- **systolic blood pressure** – the pressure when the heart is contracting

- **diastolic blood pressure** – the pressure when the heart is relaxing.

The blood pressure reading is given as the systolic reading over the diastolic reading. An average blood pressure reading is around 120 over 80 (120/80). The units are millimetres of mercury (mmHg).

# Effects of exercise

When you exercise, your working muscles need a greater supply of oxygen and, therefore, blood. A number of changes occur in the circulatory system to achieve this.

## Heart-rate changes

Your heart rate increases during exercise, depending on the intensity of the activity. An increase in exercise intensity causes a directly proportional increase in heart rate. However, each person has a maximum heart rate. When this is reached, the heart rate cannot increase further even if the exercise becomes harder. Exhaustion will occur soon after maximum heart rate is reached. Your approximate maximum heart rate can be calculated as follows:

maximum heart rate = 220 − age

For example, if you are 15, your maximum heart rate is 205.

Heart rate levels are often used by athletes to set their training intensity.

## Blood pressure

During exercise the amount of blood pumped out of your heart every minute is increased. This means that the heart is pumping harder as well as faster, and so blood pressure increases. High blood pressure when you are resting is a sign of health problems, but you need a high blood pressure during exercise to help circulate the blood. This is a perfectly healthy situation.

## Blood flow

At rest, all areas of your body receive enough blood flow to ensure they have sufficient oxygen to work. During exercise the working muscles need a much greater blood supply. This is achieved in two ways. Firstly, the heart rate increases and blood is circulated around your body at a faster rate, increasing blood flow. Secondly, the distribution of blood around the body is changed. The blood vessels leading to the working muscles expand (vasodilate) so that the extra blood flow goes to these muscles. The blood vessels leading to other areas contract (vasoconstrict) so that only the necessary amount of blood flows to these parts. This ensures that the extra blood goes to where it is needed most.

## Temperature

The amount of heat generated in your body increases during exercise. Your body has to get rid of this excess heat, to keep your body temperature stable. The heat is transported to your skin by your blood and is dispersed. During exercise, or in hot weather, sweating helps this process.

A heart-rate monitor can be used during exercise.

# 5) The digestive system

The process of breaking down the food we eat into smaller substances is called digestion. It is the function of the digestive system. The substances are then either absorbed by the body or removed from it (excreted).

## Energy from food

Energy is stored within food by being 'trapped' in the chemical bonds within the food as it is being made. Food is consumed, digested, absorbed and stored within your body.

During this process, energy is made available when the chemical bonds in which it is trapped are broken. The energy is available for various processes including movement.

Your digestive system is made up of the **gastrointestinal tract** (alimentary canal) and other **organs**. The gastrointestinal tract is 6–8 metres long in an adult. It begins with the mouth and oesophagus (food pipe), then continues into the stomach, small intestine and large intestine, and ends at the anus.

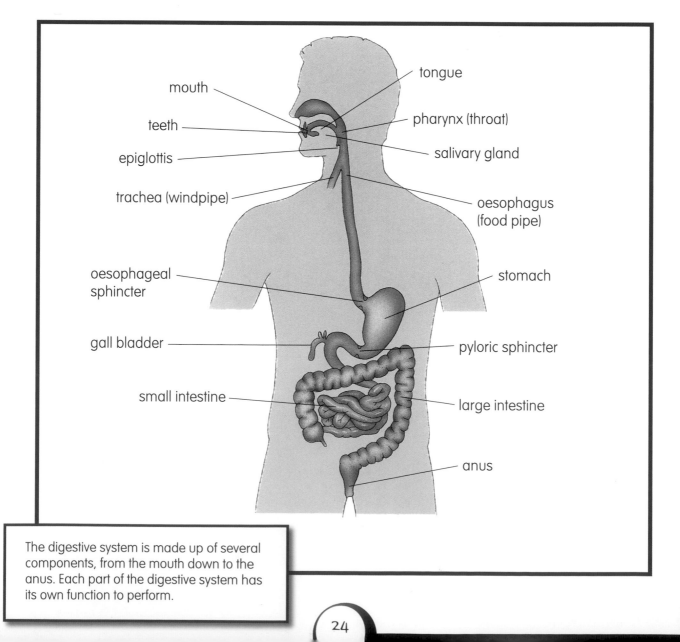

mouth

teeth

epiglottis

trachea (windpipe)

oesophageal sphincter

gall bladder

small intestine

tongue

pharynx (throat)

salivary gland

oesophagus (food pipe)

stomach

pyloric sphincter

large intestine

anus

The digestive system is made up of several components, from the mouth down to the anus. Each part of the digestive system has its own function to perform.

# Process of digestion

## Mouth

Food is taken into your mouth and chewed. The teeth grind and mash the food into smaller pieces. The food is rolled into a ball, which makes it easier to swallow.

When food enters your mouth the **salivary glands** release extra saliva. This keeps your mouth and throat moist, moistens the food and starts to break it down. Saliva contains an enzyme called **amylase** (ptyalin). This enzyme starts the process of breaking starches (or carbohydrates) down into sugars.

During swallowing, your tongue moves up and back, pushing the food into the **pharynx** (throat). The larynx (voice box) is pulled up to make the **epiglottis** close over it, which prevents food from entering the lungs.

## Oesophagus (food pipe)

After you swallow some food, it passes through the pharynx and enters the oesophagus. The food is moved along the oesophagus by the muscular action known as peristalsis. This is a wave-like action of rhythmic contractions and relaxations of the muscle along the gastrointestinal tract.

## Stomach

The food goes into your stomach through a one-way valve called the **oesophageal sphincter**. Your stomach acts as a temporary store for the partially-digested food. The stomach lining holds millions of **glands** that produce hydrochloric acid (HCl) and powerful, enzyme-containing digestive juices (gastric juices). These liquefy the food and break it down. Not very much food is absorbed in the stomach, but water, alcohol and aspirin are readily absorbed into the blood stream. This is why they have a rapid effect on the body.

On average, the stomach's volume is about 1.5 litres, but it can hold between 50 ml when 'empty' and 6 litres when full after a particularly large meal.

The contents of the stomach are mixed with acid and digestive juices to produce a slushy acidic mixture called **chyme**. The chyme gradually empties into the small intestine. After eating, the stomach takes two to three hours to empty, depending on the size and type of meal.

Stomach emptying is controlled by the opening and closing of another valve leading out of your stomach, called the **pyloric sphincter**. If after a large meal the stomach gets too stretched, signals are sent to the pyloric sphincter causing it to relax so that more chyme can leave the stomach and enter the small intestine. If the intestine gets too stretched the amount of chyme leaving the stomach is reduced.

## Producing saliva

Under normal conditions saliva is released continuously from the salivary glands. However, the amount of saliva released varies depending on the conditions. When you are dehydrated, in order to save water, saliva is not released and your mouth feels dry. This makes you feel thirsty. Food in the mouth stimulates the release of saliva as does the sight, smell, sound and feel of food.

# Small intestine

When chyme leaves your stomach it enters a passage called the small intestine. This is divided into three sections: the **duodenum** (the first 0.3 m), **jejunum** (next 1–2 m) and the **ileum** (last 1.5 m). Your pancreas is linked to the small intestine and releases juices to neutralize the acid in the chyme. Special enzymes break down more complex pieces of food. Fat is difficult to break down, and needs bile for proper digestion. Bile is produced in your liver and stored in your gall bladder. Your gall bladder releases bile into the duodenum when it is needed.

The broken-down food is absorbed into the bloodstream, along with water, alcohol, vitamins and minerals. The food passes through the walls of the small intestine and into your bloodstream. The walls of the small intestine are lined with millions of little projections called **villi**. These greatly increase the surface area between the small intestine and the blood vessels, so that more nutrients can pass into your blood and be carried to the liver. Some nutrients can be stored by the liver, and released as and when they are needed.

As the chyme moves through your small intestine (this takes from 3 to 10 hours) propulsive movements continue to churn and mix it until it reaches the sphincter into the large intestine. The indigestible waste products (the remaining 10 per cent of food) move into the large intestine.

## Large intestine

This is the final section of your gastrointestinal tract. It is about 1.2 metres long and contains no villi. It is also known as the colon or bowel. Here, water and minerals are re-absorbed. Waste fluids are taken by the blood to your kidneys, where they are filtered and pass as urine through the bladder to be excreted. Undigested food residue (faeces) are stored ready for excretion through the anus.

## Nutrition and exercise

You must consume food to supply your body with the nutrients it needs to survive. The six essential nutrients are:

- *carbohydrates* – which provide the body with energy

- *fats* – which provide stored energy and insulation

- *proteins* – which supply material for growth and repair

- *minerals* – which contribute towards growth and repair and essential body chemistry

- *vitamins* – to regulate body metabolism and development

- *water* – to transport nutrients, waste products and hormones. Water is also a major component of **cells** and plays an important role in temperature regulation.

Foods contain various proportions of these nutrients. Bread, rice, pasta and vegetables, for example, are valuable sources of carbohydrates. Butter, margarine, oils, and cheese are high in fat. Dairy products, meat, fish and nuts are valuable sources of protein.

A healthy diet includes a variety of different foods that allow the body to function at its best. Fat is an important nutrient, but unfortunately we tend to eat too much of it. This can lead to obesity and other health problems, including heart disease and cancer. Carbohydrate is the most important fuel for exercise, but we can only store a limited amount of it in muscles. Therefore, it is important that we eat enough carbohydrate every day to keep our stores high.

## Fluids

When you exercise, your body produces a lot of heat. To prevent an excessive increase in body temperature, you must get rid of this heat. Sweating helps us to do this.

Athletes who undertake high intensity exercise in hot conditions can lose 2–3 litres of sweat each hour! In a typical exercise session you can expect to lose around a litre of sweat per hour. Children and the elderly have lower sweat rates and are therefore less able to regulate their body temperatures when they are hot.

It is very difficult to rely on visible signs to show how much sweat is lost during training or sport, especially for swimmers for example! There are some specific guidelines related to replacing fluids that you should keep in mind:

• Start each session well hydrated, having replaced any fluids from a previous session.

• Have a drink about 10–15 minutes before your activity. You should be able to drink about 600–1,000 ml per hour, so you could drink about 150–250 ml every 15 minutes.

• Make sure that you have fluid intake opportunities – this could be as simple as making sure you have a bottle of water with you. Organizers of events should always provide plenty of drinks.

• Aim to drink early in the session and then at regular intervals throughout.

• Make full use of natural breaks in activities such as half-times, substitutions, time out, change of ends, etc.

• You should aim to replace about 80 per cent of the fluid lost through sweat.

• After exercise, rehydrate as quickly as possible – if you know how much you have lost then plan to drink an extra 50 per cent over the next couple of hours.

• Water is generally considered to be the best drink for rehydration. Sports drinks have been developed to provide the correct balance of carbohydrate and fluid to improve performance in high intensity sports and intermittent exercise such as team sports.

Dehydration can cause very real problems and will certainly have a negative effect on a person's performance as it reduces mental functioning and skill co-ordination. Physically, it can cause nausea, vomiting, diarrhoea and other gastrointestinal problems and also increase the risk of heat stress.

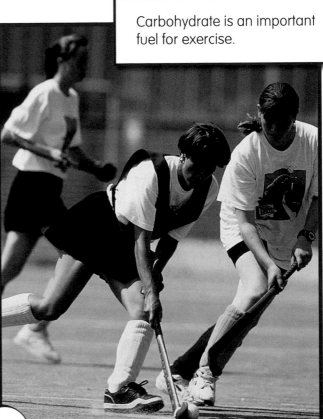

Carbohydrate is an important fuel for exercise.

# 6) The nervous system

The nervous system is one of your body's main control centres. Its function is to sense changes inside or outside the body, interpret the changes and then bring about a response. It controls all your body's movements, and has many other functions.

The nervous system is organized into:

- the central nervous system (CNS)
- the peripheral nervous system (PNS)

## Central nervous system

The central nervous system is the control centre for the entire nervous system. It consists of your brain and **spinal cord**. Information from around the body is sent to the central nervous system to be interpreted and acted upon.

### Brain

The brain is the control centre for all voluntary (conscious) and involuntary (automatic or unconscious) activities. Most movements that you make are voluntary because you choose to move. Involuntary activities include your heart beat, which occurs without you thinking about it. The brain is a very delicate **organ** that needs to be protected. This protection is given by your cranium (skull), three layers of membrane around the brain and your cerebrospinal fluid. This fluid circulates around your brain, acts as a shock absorber and helps protect the brain from injury.

Your brain has many different parts each with a special function. Three important areas are:

- **cerebrum** – the largest portion of the brain. This is responsible for conscious control of movement as well as thought, speech, memory, imagination, learning and decision-making.

- **cerebellum** – the second largest portion of the brain. This is concerned with co-ordination of movement and controls posture and balance.

- **medulla oblongata** – the lowest part of

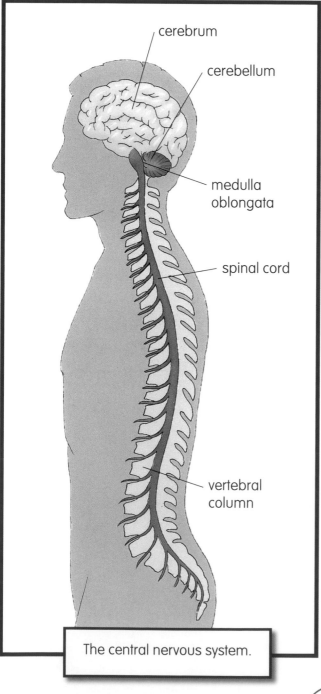

cerebrum

cerebellum

medulla oblongata

spinal cord

vertebral column

The central nervous system.

the brain stem. This connects with the spinal cord. It is responsible for involuntary activities such as breathing, digestion and heart beat.

## Spinal cord

The spinal cord is located inside your spine (vertebral column). It extends from the base of your brain to your lower back. In an adult it is about 42–45 cm long and its circumference is about 2.54 cm in the middle of the back, although it is bigger in some parts.

# Peripheral nervous system

The peripheral nervous system links the central nervous system to the **receptors**, muscles and **glands** around the body. It consists of a large network of nerves that spread out around the body.

The peripheral nervous system can be divided into:

- the sensory (afferent) system – conveys information from around the body to the central nervous system. Your ears, eyes, mouth, nose and skin all send information to the central nervous system about what you hear, see, taste, smell and feel, and it responds appropriately. These organs are called the sensory organs. During exercise you get a lot of information about your surroundings from what you see, hear and feel.

- the motor (efferent) system – conveys information from the central nervous system to your muscles and glands to bring about an action.

The nervous system helps these swimmers balance at the start of a race.

# Structure of a neurone

Nerves are made up of bundles of nerve **cells** (**neurones**) that are surrounded by **connective tissue**. Neurones are the basic unit of the nervous system and are made up of three parts:

- cell body (soma) – the main cell body that contains the nucleus

- dendrites – short projections from the cell body; their function is to conduct electrical signals called **nerve impulses** (information) towards the cell body

- axon – a single long process that conducts nerve impulses away from the cell body. At the end, the axon branches into many fine filaments called axon terminals. Axons vary in length from a few millimetres (in the brain) to one metre (between the spinal cord and the toes).

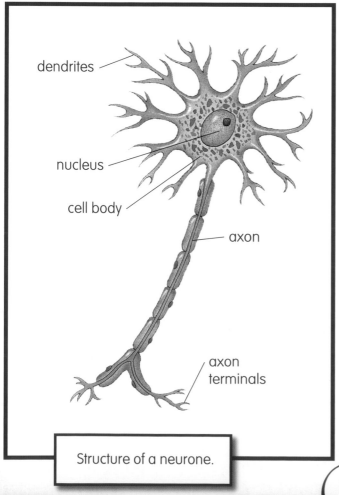

dendrites

nucleus

cell body

axon

axon terminals

Structure of a neurone.

# Impulse transmission

Neurones are able to generate and conduct nerve impulses. Information is conveyed along the nerve network by impulses being transmitted from one neurone to another, or from a neurone to a muscle or gland. The speed at which impulses are transmitted is your speed of reaction.

# Types of neurones

Some neurones are under voluntary control and some are under involuntary control:

- voluntary control – these neurones convey information from the central nervous system to skeletal muscle. You are able to control skeletal muscle so you can choose when to move.

- involuntary control – these neurones convey information from the central nervous system to smooth muscle tissue, cardiac muscle tissue and glands. This occurs without you having to think about it. The heart, blood vessels and respiratory muscles are examples of areas that are under involuntary control. This is a good thing because if you had to think about every heart beat and every breath, you would be kept very busy!

## Head injuries

When a sports person receives a blow to the head there is always a risk of concussion (temporary loss of consciousness). Any person experiencing concussion should be taken to a doctor for a proper examination.

# Control of movement

When you want to perform a movement such as bending an arm, nerve impulses are sent from the central nervous system to your arm muscles. The impulse causes the muscles to contract and the arm to bend. Impulses are also sent to other muscles to cause them to relax so that the movement can occur. The contraction and relaxation of muscles has to be co-ordinated so that the movement is smooth and controlled. This is the job of the nervous system.

Many movements that you make are in response to information that you have received from outside the body. This information comes from the sensory organs. They allow you to see, hear and feel what is going on around you. In sport you can see where other players are, hear the referee or the crowd, and feel the ball or racket.

You then use your brain to decide what action to take and how to move. Impulses will then be sent to the muscles to allow this to occur.

Not all information comes from outside the body. You also get information from receptors within your body that affect how you move. There are various receptors in the muscles, joints, **tendons** and **ligaments** that sense what is going on during movement and send information to the central nervous system about the changes occurring. These receptors are called proprioceptors. They sense information about the amount of contraction in muscles and the position of joints in space. The information from these receptors means, for example, that you can touch the end of your nose when your eyes are shut. This is because you know where your nose and hand are without looking.

## Reflex actions

A reflex action is a quick, automatic response to something. An impulse is sent rapidly from a receptor to the brain or spinal cord and directly to the muscles involved. Often the brain is by-passed. Some examples of reflexes are the knee-jerk reflex, removing a hand from a hot object and blinking in response to something touching the outside of the eye. These are essential reactions that protect the body from harm, but not all reflexes are in response to danger.

Archery requires very fine control of movement.

# The skeletal system

The skeletal system (skeleton) is the framework of bones and joints inside your body. The functions of the skeletal system are to provide support, shape, protection and movement, and to produce blood **cells**.

components such as **organs** and soft tissues. It also provides a point of attachment for many muscles and gives your body its basic shape.

## Support and shape

The skeleton provides support to keep your body upright as well as supporting its other

## Protection

Parts of your skeleton surround your vital organs and protect them from damage. The skull protects the brain, the rib cage protects

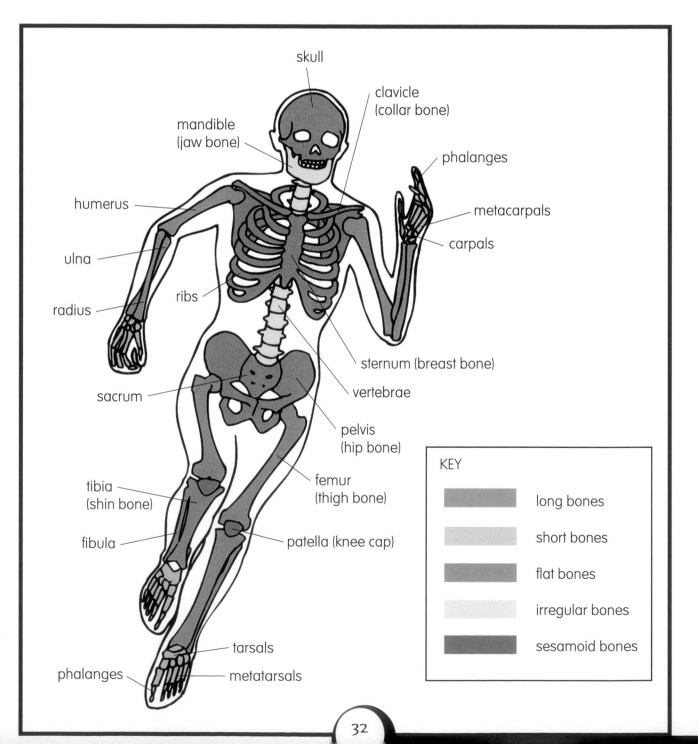

skull

clavicle (collar bone)

mandible (jaw bone)

phalanges

humerus

metacarpals

carpals

ulna

radius

ribs

sternum (breast bone)

sacrum

vertebrae

pelvis (hip bone)

tibia (shin bone)

femur (thigh bone)

fibula

patella (knee cap)

phalanges

tarsals

metatarsals

KEY

long bones

short bones

flat bones

irregular bones

sesamoid bones

the heart and lungs, the spine protects the **spinal cord** and the pelvis protects the internal reproductive organs.

# Movement

Movement takes place as a result of muscles contracting and pulling a bone about a joint. The amount of movement that can occur at a joint depends on its structure. Some joints are designed for a large range of movement, others for little or no movement.

# Blood cell production

Red blood cells are produced in the middle part (the marrow) of certain bones. Some white blood cells and platelets are also made in the marrow. The bone also stores important mineral salts such as calcium and phosphorus.

# Divisions of the skeleton

The adult skeleton is made up of 206 bones that can be divided into two parts:

• axial skeleton consisting of the skull, the thoracic cage (rib cage) and the vertebral column (spine)

• appendicular skeleton consisting of the bones of the arms and legs and of the shoulder and hip girdles that link them to the axial skeleton.

# Classification of bones

There are five main types of bone:

• long bones

• short bones

• flat bones

• irregular bones

• sesamoid bones.

## Long bones

These bones are longer than they are wide and are slightly curved for strength. The curve allows the bone to absorb the stress of the body weight at certain points and this helps prevent breaks. The femur (thigh), fibula and tibia (lower leg), humerus (upper arm), ulna and radius (forearm) and phalanges (fingers and toes) are all long bones. These bones act as levers and play an important role in movement.

## Short bones

These are almost cube-shaped because their length and width are nearly equal. The carpals (in the wrist) and tarsals (in the ankle) are short bones.

## Flat bones

These are thin, flat bones that are very important for protection. They also provide a large surface area where muscles are attached. The pectoral (shoulder) girdle, pelvic (hip) girdle, the ribs and the cranium (skull) are all flat bones.

## Irregular bones

These are irregular-shaped bones that cannot be grouped into one of the above categories. The vertebrae and certain facial bones are classed as irregular bones.

## Sesamoid bones

These are classified because of where they are rather than because of their shape. These bones are located in tendons where considerable pressure develops. The patella (knee cap) is an example of this type of bone.

# Joints

A joint is where two bones meet, where **cartilage** and bone meet or where teeth and bone meet. Movement is produced when a muscle contracts and moves a bone (lever) about a central point (fulcrum). Joints are the central point around which bones move. Joints can be classified according to how much movement they allow:

- immovable joints are fixed joints at which no movement occurs. The joints between the bones in the skull are examples of immovable joints. Such joints exist in young people to allow growth, but then become solid in adults.

- slightly movable joints permit only a little movement. Examples are the joints between vertebrae and the joint between the tibia and fibula at the ankle end of the lower leg.

- freely movable joints are **synovial joints** and permit free movement. Due to the movement permitted, these joints play an important role in any form of physical activity or exercise.

We shall now examine some of the tissues that help form the structure of joints in general.

# Connective tissues

The main function of the **connective tissues** is to bind and support various structures in the body. There are many different types of connective tissue. Three types that relate to joints are:

- cartilage, which consists of a dense network of fibres that are capable of absorbing a lot of force. There are different types of cartilage present in the body.

Hyaline cartilage is an important component of joints. It covers the joining surfaces of the bones in the joints and its job is to protect the bone and reduce friction in the joint. Other types of cartilage help maintain the shape of certain organs such as the nose, the flaps of the ear and the **epiglottis** of the larynx (voice box).

- **ligaments**, which are bands or cords of fibres that join bone to bone across a joint and restrict its movement. As a joint nears the end of its range of motion, the ligaments pull tight and stop further movement. When a joint is forced beyond its normal range of movement, the surrounding ligaments may be strained or torn. This makes the joint less stable.

- **tendons**, which are tough bands or cords of densely packed fibres similar to ligaments, but more elastic. They always make up part of a muscle and join muscle to bone allowing movement to take place.

# Synovial joints

Synovial joints have a space between the bones called the synovial cavity. This allows a greater range of movement than in other joints. There are six different types of synovial joint but they have certain common characteristics:

- articular capsule – this is a sleeve-like covering that encloses the synovial cavity and connecting bones. It is composed of two layers, an outer layer of fibres and an inner layer called the synovial membrane.

The outer layer consists of dense connective tissue that is flexible enough to allow movement yet strong enough to resist dislocation.

The synovial membrane releases synovial fluid into the joint and this acts as a lubricating fluid. It helps reduce friction and allows the joint to move more easily. The fluid also provides nutrients to the hyaline cartilage.

- hyaline cartilage – this is the type of cartilage that covers the surfaces of the connecting bones.

- ligaments – these join bone to bone and limit the range of movement in the joint.

- articular discs (menisci) – these are pads of fibro-cartilage that lie between the connecting surfaces and are attached to the fibrous capsule. They allow bones of different shapes to fit neatly together, and also act as shock absorbers.

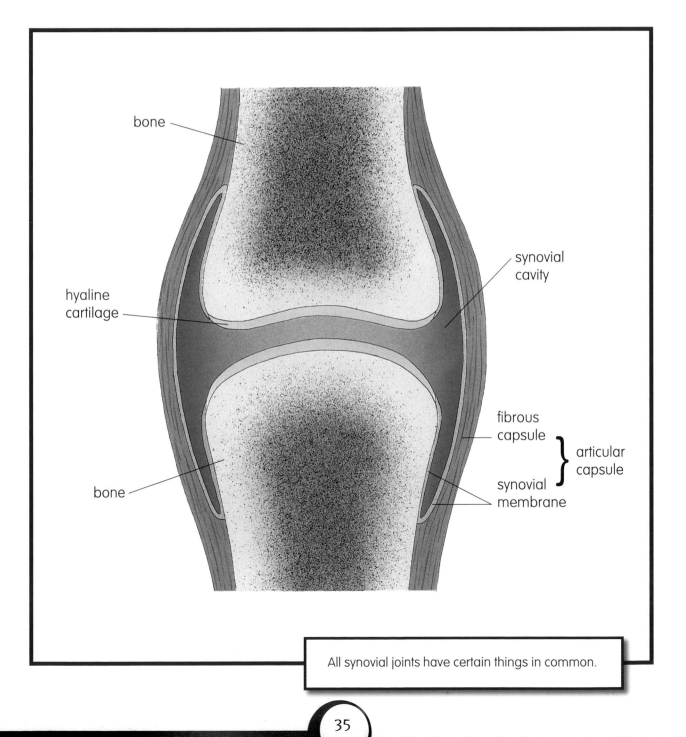

All synovial joints have certain things in common.

# Types of synovial joint

There are six types of synovial joint, each allowing different types and ranges of movement:

- *gliding joints* – joining surfaces are usually flat and glide over each other. They allow side-to-side and back-and-forth movements. They include the joints between the tarsals and the carpals, the sternum and clavicle, and the scapula and clavicle.

- *hinge joints* – a convex surface of one bone fits into the concave surface of another. They only allow movement in one direction, for example bending and straightening the elbow and finger joints.

- *pivot joints* – a rounded, pointed or cone-shaped surface of one bone fits into a ring formed by another bone and a ligament. They allow rotation, for example the joint near the elbow between the two bones in the forearm that allows the forearm to rotate.

- *condyloid or ellipsoidal joints* – an oval-shaped condyle (end) of one bone fits into an elliptical cavity of another. They allow side-to-side and back-and-forth movements. For example, the joint between the radius and carpals in the wrist.

- *saddle joints* – a special form of condyloid joint where the joining bones are shaped like a rider and a saddle. They allow side-to-side and back-and-forth movements. For example, the joint between the bones at the base of the thumb.

- *ball and socket joints* – a ball-like bone fits into a socket-like surface of another bone. They allow movement in three directions: side-to-side, back-and-forth and rotation. For example, the hip and shoulder joints.

# Range of movement and stability

The range of movement at a joint and its stability are related to each other. The immovable or slightly movable joints permit little or no movement, but are much more stable than the freely movable joints. The ball and socket joints allow the greatest range of movement but are the least stable joints. The range of movement at the hip is less than at the shoulder because of the joint surfaces and strong ligaments. The shoulder joint, in particular, is fairly unstable and so dislocation of the shoulder is a fairly common injury. This is especially the case in activities such as canoeing and contact sports, where strong movements occur at extreme positions.

The range of movement at a joint is determined by three factors:

- *muscles and tendons* – tightness of muscles limits range of motion, but this can be improved through flexibility training

- *the shape of the joining surfaces* – close-fitting bony structures limit the range of motion of a joint

- *restraining effects of ligaments* – these limit range of motion and help maintain stability.

The flexibility of a joint should not exceed the ability of the muscles to support and maintain the stability of the joint.

These diagrams show the six types of synovial joint and how each one works to allow movement.

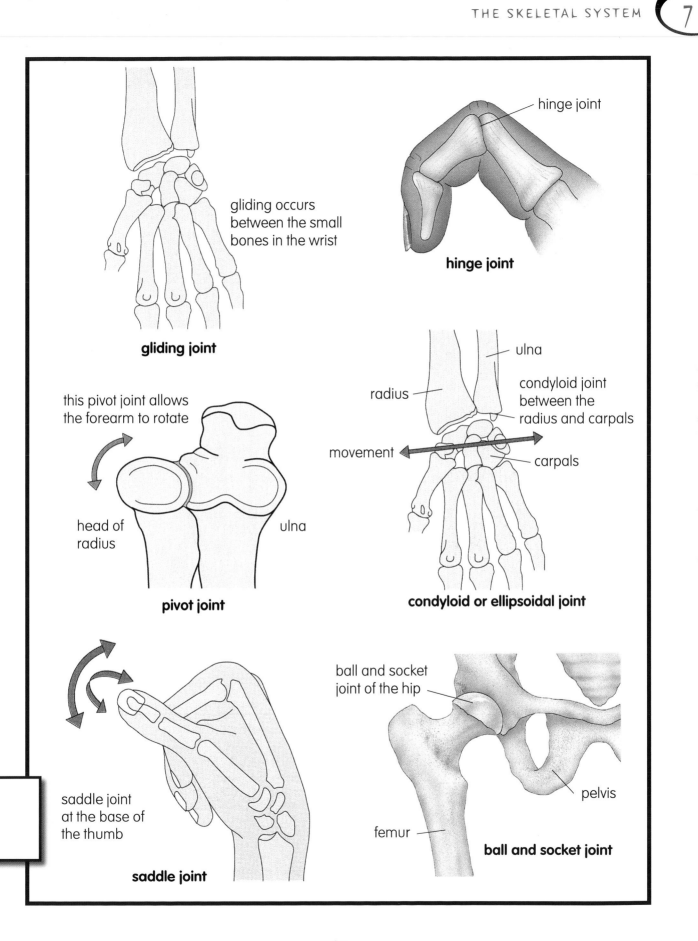

gliding occurs
between the small
bones in the wrist

**gliding joint**

hinge joint

**hinge joint**

this pivot joint allows
the forearm to rotate

head of
radius

ulna

**pivot joint**

ulna

radius

condyloid joint
between the
radius and carpals

movement

carpals

**condyloid or ellipsoidal joint**

saddle joint
at the base of
the thumb

**saddle joint**

ball and socket
joint of the hip

pelvis

femur

**ball and socket joint**

# The vertebral column

Your vertebral column (spine) is composed of a series of vertebrae and makes up about two-fifths of the total height of your body.

The functions of the vertebral column are to:

- keep the body upright

- enclose and protect the spinal cord

- support the head

- serve as a point of attachment for the ribs and muscles of the trunk

- act as a shock absorber

- contribute to movement.

The spine is divided into five regions:

- *cervical region* – there are seven cervical vertebrae located in the neck area. The first vertebra, the atlas, supports the head. The second vertebra, the axis, is the pivot on which the atlas and head rotate. The neck muscles attach here and movements of the head, such as nodding, take place in this area.

- *thoracic region* – this consists of 12 large, strong vertebrae in the chest area. These vertebrae link with the ribs and support the rib cage (except for the bottom two thoracic vertebrae). Some movement is possible in this area, but not much.

- *lumbar region* – this consists of five vertebrae which are the largest and strongest in the spine. They are located in the lower back area and their main job is to support the weight of the body. Lumbar vertebrae are well adapted for muscle attachment. Most of the back muscles attach in this area.

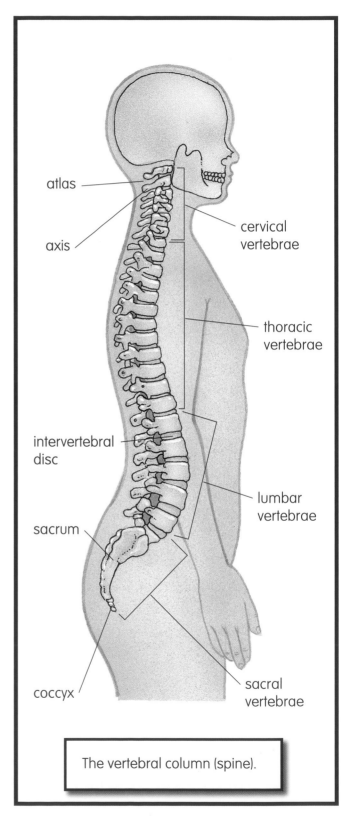

The vertebral column (spine).

• *sacral region* (*sacrum*) – this consists of five fused (joined together) vertebrae that form a triangular bone. The sacrum joins with the pelvic girdle and transfers weight from the trunk to the hips and legs. Fusion of these bones begins at 16–18 years and should be complete by the mid-20s.

• *coccyx* – this consists of four fused vertebrae and is also triangular-shaped. It is often referred to as the tail as it is located at the very bottom of the vertebral column. This region of the spine serves no function.

# Types of movement

Various types of movement are possible at different joints. Many of these movements occur in pairs and oppose each other.

## General movements

General movements are possible at a number of joints:

• *abduction* – movement of a bone away from the mid-line of the body. For example, lifting your leg out to the side.

• *adduction* – movement of a bone towards the mid-line of the body. For example, bringing your leg back in from the side.

• *extension* – increasing the angle between two bones. For example, straightening your elbow.

• *flexion* – decreasing the angle between two bones. For example, bending your elbow.

• *hyperextension* – the extension past the starting or straight position. For example, many women and girls can hyperextend their elbow past the straight-arm position.

• *inward* (*medial*) *rotation* – rotating a limb towards the mid-line of the body. For example, turning your arm inwards.

• *outward* (*lateral*) *rotation* – rotating a limb away from the mid-line of the body. For example, turning your arm outwards.

## Special movements

Special movements only occur at a particular joint:

• dorsiflexion – bending the foot up towards the shin

• plantarflexion – bending the foot downwards away from the body in the direction of the sole

• eversion – turning the sole of the foot outwards

• inversion – turning the sole of the foot inwards

• pronation – turning the forearm so that the palm faces downwards or backwards

• supination – turning the forearm so that the palm faces upwards or forwards.

Most movements that you make involve a combination of the above movements. For example, kicking a ball involves knee flexion and extension, hip flexion and extension, foot plantarflexion and dorsiflexion. In addition, movements of the arms and trunk will also take place. It is the job of the nervous system to ensure all these movements occur in a co-ordinated manner.

# 8  The muscular system

Bones and joints provide the levers and framework for movement but it is the muscles that are able to produce the movement. They do this by contracting and relaxing. Muscle contractions also help maintain posture and produce heat to maintain body temperature. There are three types of muscle in the body:

• *smooth muscle* – this type of muscle is involved in controlling things inside the body. Its contraction is not under voluntary (conscious) control and so it is called involuntary. It is found in the walls of hollow structures such as the intestines and the blood vessels.

• *cardiac muscle* – this special type of muscle makes up the walls of the heart. It is not found in any other part of the body. It is striped in appearance and is involuntary, like smooth muscle. Cardiac muscle is able to contract and relax without external nerve stimulation, so that it can keep on beating by itself.

• *skeletal muscle* – this type of muscle is mainly attached to the skeleton. It is striped in appearance and is voluntary. That means it can be made to contract and relax by conscious control.

The term 'muscular system' refers to the skeletal muscles of the body. Cardiac muscle forms the heart so is part of the circulatory system. The location of smooth muscle determines which system it is part of. Smooth muscles in the intestines are part of the digestive system, whereas smooth muscles in the blood vessels are part of the circulatory system.

Skeletal muscle is made up of bundles of muscle fibres. These fibres are cylindrical **cells** that lie parallel to each other. Muscle fibres are surrounded and separated from each other by a layer of **connective tissue** (endomysium). Each bundle of fibres is surrounded and separated from other bundles by another layer of connective tissue (perimysium). Finally, each muscle is surrounded by a further layer of connective tissue (epimysium). These layers of connective tissue continue beyond the length of the muscle and group together to form a **tendon** that then connects the muscle to a bone.

A weightlifter's skeletal muscles are strong and well defined.

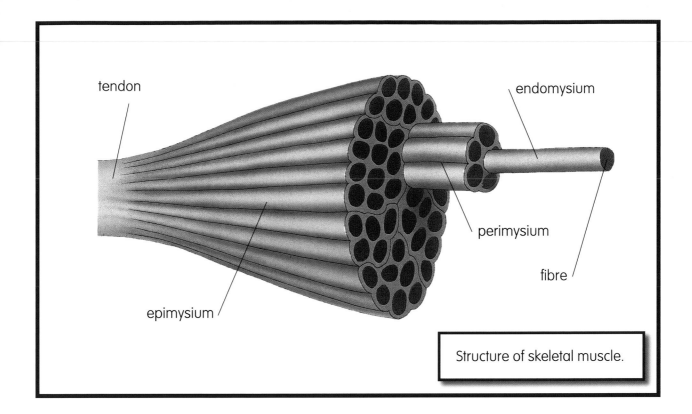

Structure of skeletal muscle.

Special terms are used to describe the points at which the tendon at either end of the muscle attaches to the bone:

- origin – the point of attachment on the bone at the end nearest the centre of the body

- insertion – the point of attachment on the bone at the end furthest from the centre of the body.

# Muscle fibre types

There are two main types of muscle fibres that are distinguished from each other by their speed of contraction:

- slow twitch fibres are so called because they contract relatively slowly. They cannot supply high levels of energy at once but they can supply a lot of energy over a period of time, and are resistant to fatigue. These fibres are therefore used for endurance activities.

- fast twitch fibres are able to contract very quickly and produce a lot of energy in an instant. However, they tire quickly. These fibres are used for activities that require speed and power, such as sprinting and jumping.

## Endurance or power?

Muscles are composed of a mixture of both muscle fibre types, but the proportions vary from person to person. These proportions appear to be relatively fixed for each person. People with high percentages of slow twitch fibres will be better at endurance activities. People with high percentages of fast twitch fibres will be better at power events such as sprints and jumps.

# Control of movement

Your muscles contract when they are stimulated by the nervous system. When you decide to make a movement such as flexing a knee a **nerve impulse** is sent from the brain to the relevant leg muscles: the hamstrings. This impulse causes the muscles to contract and shorten, which causes the knee to flex.

Muscles are only able to pull a bone towards another bone, they cannot push a bone away. This is why they work in pairs creating opposite movements.

The quadriceps muscles, when shortened, cause the opposite movement to the hamstrings by extending the leg. It is important, therefore, that these muscles do not work against each other. The nervous system makes sure this does not happen. It does this by sending a nerve impulse to the quadriceps causing them to relax at the same time as it sends the nerve impulse to the hamstrings to contract.

Throughout your body at the various joints, opposing muscles work in this way to allow movement to occur. The special terms used to describe the different roles of the muscles are:

- **agonist (prime mover)** – the muscle that contracts to produce the movement. In the above example this is the hamstrings.

- **antagonist** – the muscle that relaxes to allow the movement to occur. In the above example this is the quadriceps.

For the opposite movement, extending the leg, the muscles reverse roles. The quadriceps are now the agonist as they cause the leg to extend by contracting. The hamstrings are the antagonist as they relax to permit the movement. Muscles that work in this way are described as an antagonistic pair.

Muscles that assist the agonist and reduce any unnecessary movements are called **synergists**. Muscles that help stabilize the origin (see page 41) of the agonist are called **fixators**.

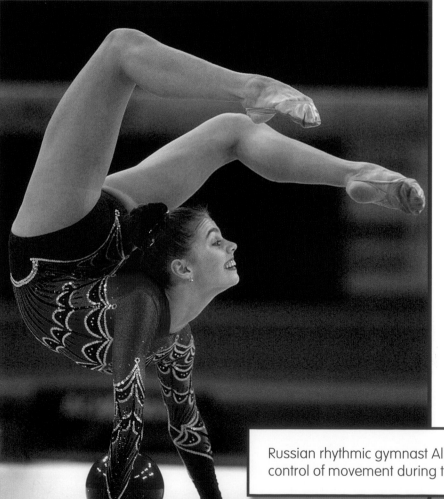

Russian rhythmic gymnast Alina Kabaeva demonstrates good control of movement during the ball apparatus competition.

# Types of muscle contraction

Normally we tend to think of a contraction as resulting in a muscle shortening. However, there are three types of muscle contraction that do not all result in the muscle shortening:

- **concentric contraction** – the muscle shortens as it develops tension and overcomes a resistance. For example in a biceps curl the biceps contracts and shortens to pull the hand towards the body.

- **isometric contraction** – in this type of contraction no movement occurs around a joint, but tension is still developed in the muscle. If you hold a heavy weight with your arms bent at right angles (as for a biceps curl) and try to keep the weight in the same position, then this is an isometric contraction. The weight acts to try to straighten the arms, therefore the biceps muscles must resist this by developing tension and keeping the weight in the same position.

- **eccentric contraction** – the muscle lengthens as it develops tension. In a biceps curl when the weight is lowered the biceps gradually lengthen. The biceps develops tension in order to control that lengthening. This is an eccentric contraction.

You can see the tension in this gymnast's arms as he holds the crucifix position.

# Muscle tone

At any given time some fibres in a muscle are contracted while others are relaxed. The number of contracting fibres may not be enough to produce movement, but they do tighten the muscle. This is called muscle tone. Muscle tone develops when stretch develops in a muscle. Stretch **receptors** sense the amount of stretch and respond by developing tone in the muscle. This helps to maintain position. For example, the muscles in the back of the neck are partially contracted (toned) to prevent the head from falling forwards and to keep it in the correct position. When you are asleep, all fibres in the muscle relax and there is no muscle tone. When you are stressed, muscle tone can increase and cause stiffness in such areas as the neck and shoulders.

# Posture

Posture is the way you hold your body. Your body needs to be held in a position that allows its different parts to function properly. Muscle tone is very important in maintaining posture.

Good posture is important for:

• sitting, standing and moving around

• activities such as dance and gymnastics where the performer wants to look good

• health

• the prevention of injuries.

Poor posture can result in damage to surrounding **organs** and tissues. Many people have lower back problems that are often due to poor posture. Slouching instead of keeping the back straight, and incorrect posture when lifting objects can result in postural problems and injuries. Stretching and strengthening the muscles that control posture can help prevent these problems.

# Categories of muscles

Just as the movements at joints are categorized, the muscles that produce those movements can be categorized in a similar way:

• abductors – the muscles that move a limb away from the mid-line of the body

• adductors – the muscles that move a limb back towards the mid-line of the body

• extensors – the muscles that increase the angle between two bones

• flexors – the muscles that decrease the angle between two bones

• rotators – the muscles that cause a limb to rotate.

| Muscle | Location | Function |
|---|---|---|
| triceps | back of the upper arm | elbow extension |
| biceps | front of the upper arm | elbow flexion |
| deltoids | on the shoulders | shoulder movements |
| pectorals | front of the upper chest | assist shoulder and upper arm movements |
| trapezius | at either side of the neck on the upper back | shoulder blade movements and head extension |
| gluteals | the bottom | abduction, adduction, rotation and extension of thigh |
| quadriceps | front of the upper leg | knee extension and hip flexion |
| hamstrings | back of the upper leg | knee flexion and hip extension |
| gastrocnemius | back of the lower leg | plantarflexion of the foot and knee flexion |
| latissimus dorsi | on the back from the middle cage to the lower back | upper arm movements. Draws arm of the rib downwards and backwards. |
| abdominals | front and side of the stomach | flexion and rotation of the trunk and to assist breathing and posture |

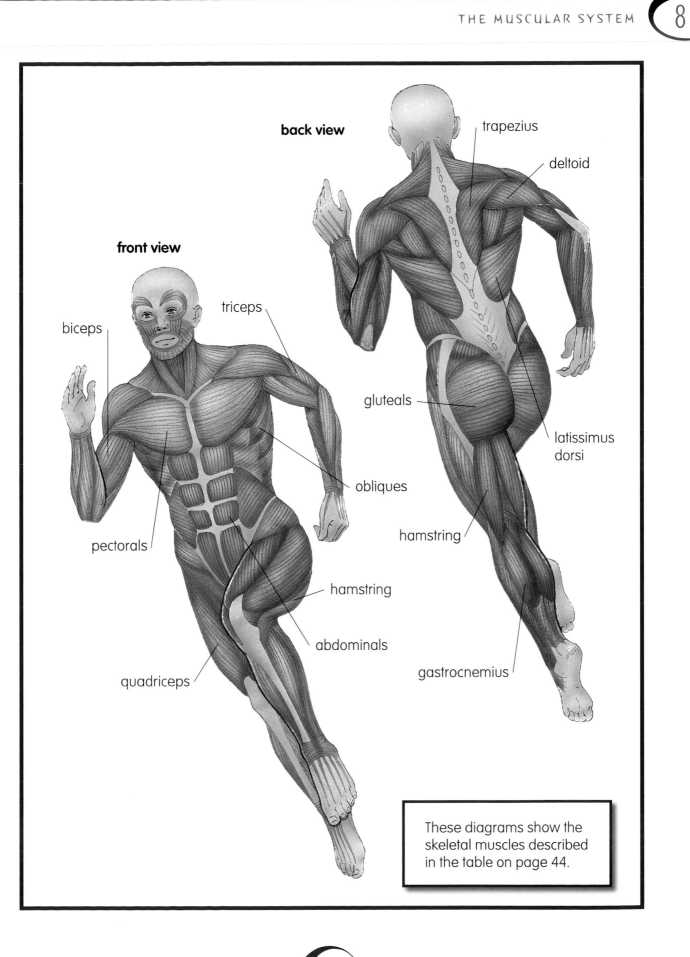

**back view**

trapezius

deltoid

**front view**

triceps

biceps

gluteals

latissimus dorsi

obliques

pectorals

hamstring

hamstring

abdominals

gastrocnemius

quadriceps

These diagrams show the skeletal muscles described in the table on page 44.

# Glossary

**aerobic** with the use of oxygen

**agonist (prime mover)** name given to a muscle that contracts to produce a movement

**alveoli** tiny air sacs that form part of the lungs

**amylase** enzyme in saliva that starts the breakdown of starches into sugars

**anaerobic** without the use of oxygen

**antagonist** name given to a muscle that relaxes to allow a movement to occur

**aorta** large blood vessel that carries oxygenated blood out of the left ventricle of the heart on its way around the body

**arterioles** small arteries that branch off from larger arteries and lead to the tissues of the body

**atherosclerosis** accumulation of fat on the walls of an artery

**atria** (or **auricles**) the two upper chambers of the heart, right atrium and left atrium

**bicuspid (mitral) valve** one-way valve in the heart separating the left atrium from the left ventricle

**capillaries** tiny blood vessels that link arterioles and venules and allow exchange of materials between blood and body cells

**cartilage** dense network of fibres that are capable of absorbing considerable stresses

**cell** basic unit of life that can maintain itself, grow and reproduce

**cerebellum** second largest portion of the brain, responsible for co-ordination of movement

**cerebrum** largest portion of the brain, responsible for conscious control of the body

**chyme** slushy acid mix produced in the stomach from food, acid and digestive juices

**concentric contraction** type of muscle contraction during which the muscle shortens as it develops tension

**connective tissue** type of tissue that binds parts of the body together

**diaphragm** large dome-shaped muscle beneath the lungs that plays an important role in breathing

**diastolic blood pressure** pressure of the blood when the heart is relaxing

**diffusion** movement of particles from an area of high concentration to an area of low concentration

**duodenum** first section of the small intestine

**eccentric contraction** type of muscle contraction during which the muscle lengthens as it develops tension

**epiglottis** flap at the top of the larynx that allows air in, and keeps food out

**fixator** name given to a muscle that helps stabilize the origin of the agonist (prime mover)

**gastrointestinal tract** tube running from the mouth to the anus, also called the alimentary canal

**gland** organ or cell that makes chemical substances and releases them for the body to use or excrete

**haemoglobin** component of red blood cells

**ileum** final section of the small intestine

**internal and external intercostals** muscles between the ribs that are involved in breathing

**isometric contraction** type of muscle contraction during which no movement occurs around a joint but tension is still developed in the muscle

**jejunum** middle section of the small intestine

**ligament** band or cord of fibrous tissue that joins bone to bone across a joint and limits the range of movement

**lumen** centre of an artery or vein

**medulla oblongata** part of the brain that connects with the spinal cord, responsible for involuntary activities such as breathing

**mucous membrane** thin layer of tissue that releases a thick fluid called mucus

**nerve impulse** electrical signal that sends information along a nerve

**neurone** nerve cell, the basic unit of the nervous system

**oesophageal sphincter** one-way valve between the oesophagus (food pipe) and the stomach

**organ** collection of different tissues that acts as a functional unit

**oxygen debt** the extra oxygen taken in during recovery from exercise

**pharynx** throat

**pleural membrane** double-layered membrane that surrounds the lungs

**pulmonary artery** large blood vessel that carries deoxygenated blood out of the right ventricle of the heart to the lungs

**pulmonary vein** large blood vessel that carries oxygenated blood into the left atrium of the heart from the lungs

**pyloric sphincter** one-way valve between the stomach and the small intestine

**receptors** parts of the nervous system that are sensitive to changes

**salivary glands** glands that release saliva into the mouth to moisten the mouth and throat and to moisten food and start to break it down

**semilunar valve** one-way valve in the aorta and pulmonary artery that stops blood flowing back into the heart

**spinal cord** nerve tissue located in the spinal column

**spirometer** device for measuring gas volumes

**superior and inferior vena cava** large blood vessels that carry deoxygenated blood from around the body into the right atrium of the heart

**synergist** muscle that assists the agonist (prime mover) by reducing any unnecessary movements

**synovial joint** joint with a space (synovial cavity) in between the bones that allows a large range of movement

**systolic blood pressure** pressure of the blood when the heart is contracting

**tendons** tough bands or cords of densely packed fibres that are part of a muscle and join muscle to bone

**tricuspid valve** one-way valve in the heart separating the right atrium and right ventricle

**vasoconstriction** decrease in the size of the lumen of a blood vessel

**vasodilation** increase in the size of the lumen in a blood vessel

**ventricles** the two lower chambers of the heart, right and left ventricle

**venules** small veins that unite to connect capillaries to veins

**villi** special protruding structures that line the small intestine and through which compounds are absorbed into the bloodstream

# Find out more

## Books

*Body Focus: Bones*, Carol Ballard (Heinemann Library, 2004)

*DK Guide: Human Body*, Richard Walker (DK Publishing, 2006)

*Making Healthy Food Choices: Food for Sport*, Neil Morris (Heinemann Library, 2006)

*Making of a Champion: A World-Class Sprinter*, Clive Gifford (Heinemann Library, 2005)

*Science on File: Human Body*, Anna Claybourne (Evans Brothers Ltd, 2006)

*Teen Issues: Fitness*, Joanna Watson and Joanna Kedge (Raintree, 2005)

## Websites

British Olympic Association: www.olympics.org.uk
BBC online:
www.bbc.co.uk/science/humanbody
www.bbc.co.uk/learning/subjects/sports_and_fitness.shtml

# Index